Fun in the sun

2

Sam, Dan and Nat
go in the sun.

Mum has a sun hat.

Dad has a dip.

Up, up, up.

Nat hits it.

Sam gets up on top.

Dan digs a big pit.

It is fun.
It is hot.

Before reading

Say the sounds: g o b h e r f u l
Ensure the children use the pure sounds for the consonants without the added
"uh" sound, e.g. "llll" not "luh".

Practise blending the sounds: hot sun hits fun hat rub dip top pit digs Dan
fun Sam Nat

High-frequency words: Dad in Mum on it up big and did
Tricky words: the is go has I

Vocabulary check: rub – Can children act out rubbing sun cream onto their
arm? pit – This is a large hole in the ground.

Story discussion: Look at the cover. Where do you think the children are? Have
you been to the beach? What are some fun things you can do there?

Teaching points: Review the purpose and use of commas in a sentence so that
children know that there is a small pause. Review the use of an exclamation
mark to show excitement or surprise. Look at the example on page 10 and
model what Sam says with and without noting the punctuation.
Review the use of speech and thought bubbles.

After reading

Comprehension:
- What did Mum want the children to do at the start of the story? Why?
- What are some of the things the family did at the beach?
- How do you think the children were feeling at the end of the story?
- What else might they do while they are at the beach?

Fluency: Speed read the words again from the inside front cover.